You're so Smart, Snoopy

Charles M. Schulz

Selected cartoons from
You're out of sight, Charlie Brown, Vol 1

CORONET BOOKS
Hodder Fawcett, London

Printed in Great Britain for Hodder
Fawcett Ltd., Mill Road, Dunton Green,
Sevenoaks, Kent. (Editorial Office:
47 Bedford Square, London, WC1 3DP) by
C. Nicholls & Company Ltd.
The Philips Park Press, Manchester

ISBN 0 340 19927 X

THE PRINCIPAL'S OFFICE? YES, MA'AM..

NOW, WHAT IN THE WORLD DOES THE PRINCIPAL WANT TO SEE **ME** ABOUT? MAYBE HE WANTS ME TO MANAGE THE SCHOOL BALL TEAM THIS NEXT SEASON...I DOUBT IT..

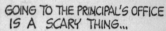

GOING TO THE PRINCIPAL'S OFFICE IS A SCARY THING...

I THINK THEY PURPOSELY PUT THE DOOR KNOB UP HIGH TO MAKE YOU FEEL INFERIOR!

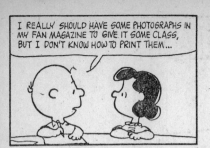

I REALLY SHOULD HAVE SOME PHOTOGRAPHS IN MY FAN MAGAZINE TO GIVE IT SOME CLASS, BUT I DON'T KNOW HOW TO PRINT THEM...

LAST YEAR JOE BATTED .143 AND MADE SOME SPECTACULAR CATCHES OF ROUTINE FLY BALLS. HE ALSO THREW OUT A RUNNER WHO HAD FALLEN DOWN BETWEEN FIRST AND SECOND.

WELL, FANS, THERE IT IS. REMEMBER, THIS LITTLE OL' FAN MAGAZINE IS YOURS. WE WELCOME YOUR COMMENTS.

WHO NEEDS IT?

I SHOULDN'T HAVE WELCOMED HER COMMENTS...

SCHULZ

QUICK, CHARLIE BROWN, GO TO THE FRONT DOOR...

TED WILLIAMS IS THERE TO SEE YOU.. HE WANTS SOME ADVICE ON HOW TO MANAGE A BASEBALL TEAM

APRIL FOOL!
HA HA HAHAHAHAHA

IT COULD HAVE HAPPENED

SNOOPY, I HAVE A SPECIAL JOB FOR YOU..

SEE IF WE HAVE ANY NEW PLAYERS TRYING OUT FOR THE TEAM... IF WE DO, GIVE THEM A LITTLE COACHING...

ROOKIE OF THE YEAR!

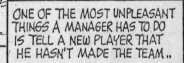

THAT'S A NICE BALLOON

THANK YOU..

WHAT DOES IT DO?

IT DOESN'T DO ANYTHING EXCEPT MAYBE FLY IF I LET GO OF IT..

WHY DON'T YOU PAINT THE WORD "LOVE" ON IT, AND LET IT FLY OFF SOMEPLACE?

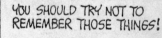

POW!

THAT'S THE LONGEST HOME RUN EVER HIT IN THIS PARK, CHARLIE BROWN, AND YOU WERE THE PITCHER..

THAT MEANS YOUR NAME WILL GO DOWN IN THE RECORD BOOKS

LOOK UNDER "GOAT"

YOU HAVE TO MOVE YOUR FEET, TOO!

HOW EMBARRASSING!

It was a dark and
stormy night.

Suddenly, a shot rang
out. A door slammed.
The maid screamed.

Suddenly, a pirate ship
appeared on the horizon!

While millions of people were starving, the king lived in luxury.

Meanwhile, on a small farm in Kansas, a boy was growing up.

Part II

IN PART TWO, I TIE ALL OF THIS TOGETHER..

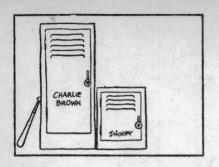

WHAT'S THIS?

"PROPOSED NEW DOG-FEEDING SCHEDULE"

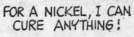

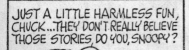

It Was a
Dark and Stormy
Night
by SNOOPY

It was a dark
and stormy night

Suddenly a shot rang out.
A door slammed. The maid
screamed. Suddenly a pirate
ship appeared on the horizon.
While millions of people
were starving, the king
lived in luxury.

Meanwhile, on a small farm in
Kansas, a boy was growing up.
End of Part I

Part II
A light snow was falling, and the little girl with the tattered shawl had not sold a violet all day.

At that very moment, a young intern at City Hospital was making an important discovery.

I MAY HAVE WRITTEN MYSELF INTO A CORNER...

WELL! DID THAT NASTY OL' POP FLY AWAKEN YOU? DID IT DISTURB YOUR BEAUTY SLEEP?

I'M SORRY IF THE SOUND OF FLY BALLS LANDING BEHIND YOU IS DEPRIVING YOU OF YOUR REST!

PERHAPS WE SHOULD SOFTEN THE INFIELD SO THE BALL WON'T MAKE SO MUCH NOISE WHEN IT LANDS BEHIND YOU...

WAAH!

OH, GOOD GRIEF! NOW, I'VE HURT HIS FEELINGS...

I'M SORRY, SNOOPY.. I APOLOGIZE.. I SHOULDN'T HAVE BEEN SO SARCASTIC.. I GUESS I DON'T KNOW HOW TO HANDLE PLAYERS...I'M A TERRIBLE MANAGER.... I APOLOGIZE..

SNIF

Z

BONK

SCHULZ

OKAY, TEAM! THAT PROVES WE'RE NOT SO BAD AFTER ALL! LET'S GET OUT THERE NOW AND WIN THIS GAME...LET'S SHOW 'EM HOW TO PLAY!

BONK!

I KNOW WHAT AWARD I'LL WIN.."STOMACH-ACHE OF THE YEAR"!

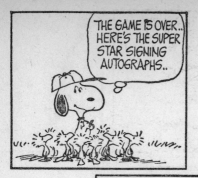

It was a dark and stormy night. Suddenly a shot rang out. A door slammed. The maid screamed.

Suddenly a pirate ship appeared on the horizon. While millions of people were starving, the king lived in luxury. Meanwhile, on a small farm in Kansas, a boy was growing up.
End of Part I

Part II.... A light snow was falling, and the little girl with the tattered shawl had not sold a violet all day.

At that very moment, a young intern at City Hospital was making an important discovery. The mysterious patient in Room 213 had finally awakened. She moaned softly.

Could it be that she was the sister of the boy in Kansas who loved the girl with the tattered shawl who was the daughter of the maid who had escaped from the pirates? The intern frowned.

SEE HOW NEATLY ALL OF THIS FITS TOGETHER?

BUT WHAT ABOUT THE KING?

BONK!

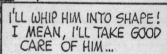

HOME AT LAST!

I'VE GOT TO GO GET SNOOPY! IF THAT LUCY WAS MEAN TO HIM, I'LL NEVER FORGIVE MYSELF

I NEVER SHOULD HAVE LEFT HIM WITH HER .. WHY DID I DO IT? WHY?

IF THAT'S GENERAL PERSHING, TELL HIM I'M BUSY!

IT'S GOOD TO BE BACK WITH MY OLD OUTFIT!

SUDDENLY, I FEEL RIDICULOUS!

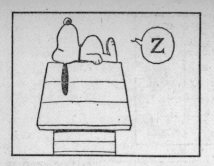

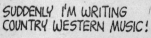

It was a dark and stormy night.

MY NEW NOVEL IS GOING BADLY...

I'VE FINISHED THE DRAWING FOR THE COVER OF YOUR NEW NOVEL..

SEE? IT SHOWS A BUNCH OF PIRATES AND FOREIGN LEGIONNAIRES FIGHTING SOME COWBOYS, AND SOME LIONS AND TIGERS AND ELEPHANTS LEAPING THROUGH THE AIR TOWARD A GIRL WHO IS TIED TO A SUBMARINE

DID HE LIKE YOUR DRAWING?

IT NEEDS MORE TIGERS!

THE WONDERFUL WORLD OF PEANUTS

☐	12544 6	What Next, Charlie Brown (26)	60p
☐	15135 8	You're the Greatest, Charlie Brown (27)	60p
☐	15829 8	It's For You Snoopy (28)	50p
☐	15828 X	Have It Your Way, Charlie Brown (29)	50p
☐	15698 8	You're Not For Real Snoopy (30)	50p
☐	15696 1	You're a Pal, Snoopy (31)	60p
☐	16712 2	What Now Charlie Brown (32)	50p
☐	17322 X	You're Something Special Snoopy (33)	50p
☐	17417 X	You've Got A Friend, Charlie Brown (34)	50p
☐	17844 2	Take It Easy, Charlie Brown (35)	50p
☐	17861 2	Who Was That Dog I Saw You With, Charlie Brown? (36)	50p
☐	18303 9	There's No-one like you Snoopy (37)	60p
☐	18663 1	Your Choice Snoopy (38)	50p
☐	18831 6	Try It Again Charlie Brown (39)	50p
☐	19550 9	You've Got It Made Snoopy (40)	50p
☐	19858 3	Don't Give Up Charlie Brown (41)	50p
☐	19927 X	You're So Smart Snoopy (42)	60p
☐	20491 5	You're On Your Own Snoopy (43)	60p
☐	20754 X	You Can't Win Them All Charlie Brown (44)	50p
☐	21236 5	It's All Yours Snoopy (45)	50p
☐	21797 9	Watch Out Charlie Brown (46)	50p
☐	21983 1	You've Got To Be You, Snoopy (47)	50p
☐	22159 3	You've Come a Long Way, Snoopy (48)	60p
☐	22304 9	That's Life Snoopy (49)	50p
☐	22778 8	It's Your Turn Snoopy (50)	50p

Numbers 1-25 and all the above Peanuts titles are available at your local bookshop or newsagent, or can be ordered direct from the publisher. Just tick the titles you want and fill in the form below.
Prices and availability subject to change without notice.

CORONET BOOKS, P.O. Box 11, Falmouth, Cornwall.
Please send cheque or postal order, and allow the following for postage and packing:
U.K.—One book 22p plus 10p per copy for each additional book ordered, up to a maximum of 82p.
B.F.P.O. and EIRE—22p for the first book plus 10p per copy for the next 6 books, thereafter 4p per book.

OTHER OVERSEAS CUSTOMERS—30p for the first book and 10p per copy for each additional book.

Name ....

Address ....

....